Magical Scenes from Shakespeare's
A Midsummer Night's Dream

Titania

Oberon

Puck

Hermia

Helena

Demetrius

Lysander

Nick Bottom

Fairies: Peaseblossom, Cobweb, Moth, Mustardseed

Introducing the story of *A Midsummer Night's Dream* ...

A long time ago, in Athens, a girl named Hermia loved a poet called Lysander. The couple wanted to marry, but Hermia's father wanted his daughter to marry a nobleman named Demetrius. Demetrius had once been in love with Hermia's best friend, Helena, but now he had thrown Helena aside for the chance to marry Hermia.

One night Hermia told Lysander that her father, and the city's ruler Duke Theseus, both said she had to marry Demetrius or become a nun. They decided to meet in the forest the next night so they could run away together and secretly marry ...

... In another part of the city, a carpenter called Peter Quince has gathered his friends to put on a play for Duke Theseus. One of the group is a weaver called Bottom. The men agree to meet the next night in the forest ... the very forest where Hermia and Lysander have agreed to meet.

Before the humans arrive, the forest is already alive with bands of fairies and other strange creatures. One of these is a mischief-loving hobgoblin known as Puck. Puck tells a fairy that his master, Oberon, the Fairy King, will soon arrive. Oberon and Titania, the Fairy Queen, are arguing about a human boy who Titania took from an Indian King. Oberon wants the boy to enter his service.

What might the characters be thinking ...?

"I must hurry and find dewdrops for my mistress Titania, the Fairy Queen."

"My master Oberon, the Fairy King, will be here soon too. The Queen should stay away from him. He is very angry with her for taking the human child that he wanted."

Useful words ...

pale a fence or hedge

orbs fairy rings; mushroom circles

lob of spirits a crude or ugly hobgoblin

passing fell and wrath wanting revenge and angry

changeling a fairy child exchanged secretly for a human infant

train servants

trace wander or roam

they do square they are assessing each other ready for a fight

A wood near Athens

Enter, from opposite sides, a Fairy, and Puck

PUCK   How now, spirit! whither wander you?

FAIRY   Over hill, over dale,
Through bush, through brier,
Over park, over **pale**,
Through flood, through fire,
I do wander everywhere,
Swifter than the moon's sphere;
And I serve the Fairy Queen,
To dew her **orbs** upon the green.
I must go seek some dewdrops here
And hang a pearl in every cowslip's ear.
Farewell, thou **lob of spirits**; I'll be gone:
Our Queen and all our elves come here anon.

PUCK   The King doth keep his revels here to-night:
Take heed the Queen come not within his sight;
For Oberon is **passing fell and wrath**,
Because that she as her attendant hath
A lovely boy, stolen from an Indian king;
She never had so sweet a **changeling**;
And jealous Oberon would have the child
Knight of his **train**, to **trace** the forests wild;
But she perforce withholds the loved boy,
Crowns him with flowers and makes him all her joy:
And now they never meet in grove or green,
By fountain clear, or spangled starlight sheen,
But, **they do square**, that all their elves for fear
Creep into acorn-cups and hide them there …
But, room, Fairy! here comes Oberon.

FAIRY   And here my mistress. Would that he were gone!

3

The story ...

Oberon asks again for the child to be his servant. Titania says that she wants to keep the boy and bring him up. They argue fiercely.

What might the characters be thinking ...?

"I won't let Oberon have this boy! He thinks he can have whatever he wants."

"Why such fuss over a mere human boy I want for my servant?"

Useful words ...

forsworn given up

henchman servant

the fairy land buys not the whole of fairyland could not buy

votaress follower

perchance probably

round a dance in a ring

revels celebrations

spare your haunts never go where you go

chide quarrel

Enter, from one side, Oberon, with his train; from the other, Titania, with hers

OBERON	Ill met by moonlight, proud Titania.
TITANIA	What, jealous Oberon! Fairies, skip hence: I have **forsworn** his bed and company …
OBERON	… Why should Titania cross her Oberon? I do but beg a little changeling boy, To be my **henchman**.
TITANIA	Set your heart at rest: **The fairy land buys not** the child of me. His mother was a **votaress** of my order … But she, being mortal, of that boy did die; And for her sake do I rear up her boy, And for her sake I will not part with him.
OBERON	How long within this wood intend you stay?
TITANIA	**Perchance** till after Theseus' wedding-day. If you will patiently dance in our **round** And see our moonlight **revels**, go with us; If not, shun me, and I will **spare your haunts**.
OBERON	Give me that boy, and I will go with thee.
TITANIA	Not for thy fairy kingdom. Fairies, away! We shall **chide** downright, if I longer stay.

Exit Titania with her train

5

The story ...

When Titania has gone, Oberon turns to Puck, and tells him to fetch a special flower juice. This juice, when squeezed upon someone's sleeping eyelids, will make them fall madly in love with the first creature they see on waking.

Puck races off to find the juice.

Helena and Demetrius arrive. Oberon, who is invisible to them, decides to listen to their conversation.

What might the characters be thinking ...?

"I'll drop this juice on to Titania's eyes. The next thing she sees, whatever kind of animal it is, she will fall in love with. And I won't remove the charm until the child is mine. That'll show her!"

"Another mission to perform. I must get going or he'll be angry with me!"

Useful words ...

madly dote be madly in love with

leviathan a sea monster

league about 3 miles

girdle a belt

liquor juice

render give

conference conversation

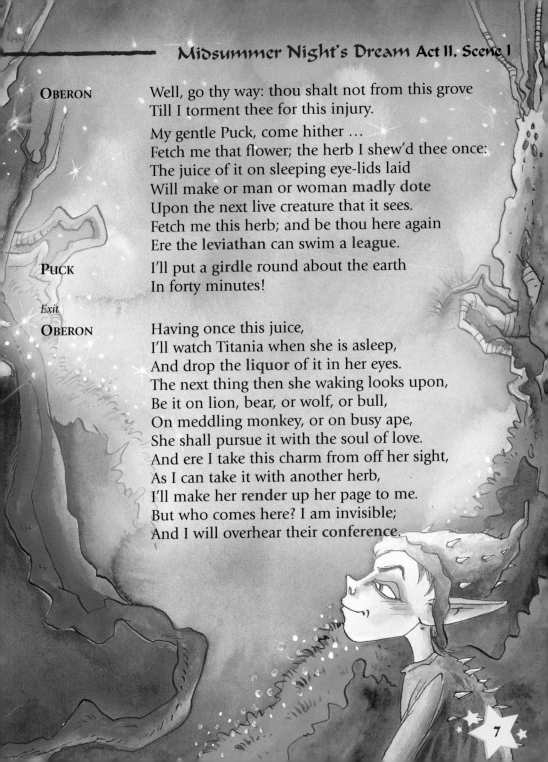

OBERON

Well, go thy way: thou shalt not from this grove
Till I torment thee for this injury.

My gentle Puck, come hither …
Fetch me that flower; the herb I shew'd thee once:
The juice of it on sleeping eye-lids laid
Will make or man or woman **madly dote**
Upon the next live creature that it sees.
Fetch me this herb; and be thou here again
Ere the **leviathan** can swim a **league**.

PUCK

I'll put a **girdle** round about the earth
In forty minutes!

Exit

OBERON

Having once this juice,
I'll watch Titania when she is asleep,
And drop the **liquor** of it in her eyes.
The next thing then she waking looks upon,
Be it on lion, bear, or wolf, or bull,
On meddling monkey, or on busy ape,
She shall pursue it with the soul of love.
And ere I take this charm from off her sight,
As I can take it with another herb,
I'll make her **render** up her page to me.
But who comes here? I am invisible;
And I will overhear their **conference**.

The story ...

Demetrius scorns Helena, and tells her to stop following him. He storms from the clearing to continue his search for Hermia, the woman he wants to marry, and Lysander, who he knows is with her. Helena is so sick with love for Demetrius that she cannot leave him and runs after him.

What might the characters be thinking ...?

"I told Helena plainly that I don't love her, so why does she insist on following me? Has she no shame? I shall have to be cruel to get rid of her."

"Demetrius can treat me like his dog. I will still dote on him."

Useful words ...

slayeth kills

stolen unto secretly come to

wode mad

brakes dense undergrowth

to die upon the hand to be killed by the hand

Enter Demetrius, Helena

DEMETRIUS   I love thee not, therefore pursue me not.
Where is Lysander and fair Hermia?
The one I'll slay, the other **slayeth** me.
Thou told'st me they were **stolen unto** this wood;
And here am I, and **wode** within this wood,
Because I cannot meet my Hermia.
Hence, get thee gone, and follow me no more.
… do I not in plainest truth
Tell you, I do not nor I cannot love you?

HELENA   And even for that do I love you the more.
I am your spaniel; and, Demetrius,
The more you beat me, I will fawn on you.
Use me but as your spaniel, spurn me, strike me,
Neglect me, lose me; only give me leave,
Unworthy as I am, to follow you …

DEMETRIUS   Tempt not too much the hatred of my spirit;
For I am sick when I do look on thee.

HELENA   And I am sick when I look not on you. …

DEMETRIUS   I'll run from thee and hide me in the **brakes**,
And leave thee to the mercy of wild beasts. …

Exit Demetrius

HELENA   I'll follow thee and make a heaven of hell,
To die upon the hand I love so well.

Exit

9

The story ...

Having seen Helena and Demetrius, Oberon sees
another use for the flower he has sent Puck to fetch. Oberon
will drop the flower's juice on to Titania's eyelids while she is
sleeping. He sends Puck to find Helena and Demetrius, and
squeeze the juice on to Demetrius' eyelids so that when he
wakes up he will love Helena even more than she loves him.
Oberon tells Puck that he will know Demetrius by his
clothing, which is that of a nobleman from Athens.

What might the characters be thinking ...?

"I can have two lots of fun with this
juice! I'll place a charm on Titania.
But I'll also help that poor woman
by making the man she loves fall in
love with her."

"More orders to obey! But this
could be fun!"

Useful words ...

over-canopied covered over by

thyme, oxlips, violet, woodbine, musk-rose, eglantine
all herbs or flowers

sometime of for sometime

disdainful scornful, mocking

anoint put drops on

espies sees

Re-enter Puck and Oberon

OBERON   … Hast thou the flower there? Welcome, wanderer.

PUCK   Ay, there it is.

OBERON   I pray thee, give it me.
I know a bank where the wild **thyme** blows,
Where **oxlips** and the nodding **violet** grows,
Quite **over-canopied** with luscious **woodbine**,
With sweet **musk-roses** and with **eglantine**:
There sleeps Titania **sometime of** the night,
Lull'd in these flowers with dances and delight; …
And with the juice of this I'll streak her eyes,
And make her full of hateful fantasies.
Take thou some of it, and seek through this grove:
A sweet Athenian lady is in love
With a **disdainful** youth: **anoint** his eyes;
But do it when the next thing he **espies**
May be the lady: thou shalt know the man
By the Athenian garments he hath on.
Effect it with some care, that he may prove
More fond on her than she upon her love.
And look thou meet me ere the first cock crow.

PUCK   Fear not, my lord, your servant shall do so.

Exeunt

The story ...

The fairies sing a lullaby to Titania who falls asleep. As she sleeps, Oberon squeezes the magical flower juice upon her eyelids.

What might the characters be thinking ...?

"Now I'll have my way. Whatever Titania sees first when she wakes up, she'll fall in love with. I'll add to the spell to make sure she wakes up when something really ugly is around!"

"I'm tired now. Mmm ... what lovely singing."

Useful words ...

roundel a dance in a ring

offices duties, jobs

languish pine with love

ounce a lynx, or any animal of the cat family

pard leopard

12

Another part of the wood

Enter Titania, with her train

TITANIA Come now, a **roundel** and a fairy song;
… Sing me now asleep;
Then to your **offices** and let me rest.

THE FAIRIES *(singing)*
You spotted snakes with double tongue,
Thorny hedgehogs, be not seen;
Newts and blind-worms, do no wrong,
Come not near our Fairy Queen …
Lulla, lulla, lullaby, lulla, lulla, lullaby:
Weaving spiders, come not here;
Hence, you long-legg'd spinners, hence!
Beetles black, approach not near;
Worm nor snail, do no offence.
Lulla, lulla, lullaby, lulla, lulla, lullaby.

Exeunt Fairies. Titania sleeps

Enter Oberon and squeezes the flower on Titania's eyelids

OBERON What thou seest when thou dost wake,
Do it for thy true-love take,
Love and **languish** for his sake:
Be it **ounce**, or cat, or bear,
Pard, or boar with bristled hair,
In thy eye that shall appear
When thou wakest, it is thy dear:
Wake when some vile thing is near!

Exit

The story ...

Meanwhile the lovers Lysander and Hermia have lost their way in the wood and are tired of wandering. They decide to rest. Because they are not yet married, Hermia asks Lysander to lie down a small distance away from her. When Puck sees Lysander lying alone, he mistakes him for Demetrius, deliberately trying to stay apart from Helena. Puck squeezes the magical flower over Lysander's eyes.

What might the characters be thinking ...?

 "We are lost. We need to rest. I'm worried about Hermia – she looks tired. We need to lie down."

 "I am tired. But I must remember to do things properly! I'll make Lysander sleep over there."

 "At last I've found the nobleman from Athens! I'll do as my master said and place the charm upon him."

Useful words ...

troth truth

tarry wait

weeds clothes

churl a rude, rough man

Enter Lysander and Hermia

LYSANDER   Fair love, you faint with wandering in the wood;
And to speak **troth**, I have forgot our way:
We'll rest us, Hermia, if you think it good,
And **tarry** for the comfort of the day.

HERMIA   Be it so, Lysander: find you out a bed;
For I upon this bank will rest my head.

LYSANDER   One turf shall serve as pillow for us both …

HERMIA   Nay, good Lysander; for my sake, my dear,
Lie further off yet, do not lie so near …

They sleep

Enter Puck

PUCK   Through the forest have I gone.
But Athenian found I none,
On whose eyes I might approve
This flower's force in stirring love.
Night and silence. – Who is here?
Weeds of Athens he doth wear:
This is he, my master said,
Despised the Athenian maid;
And here the maiden, sleeping sound,
On the dank and dirty ground. …
Churl, upon thy eyes I throw
All the power this charm doth owe …

So awake when I am gone;
For I must now to Oberon.

Exit

15

The story ...

Helena is out of breath from chasing Demetrius through the wood. She comes across Lysander who is sleeping. She fears he is sick or wounded and wakes him up. Immediately Lysander falls in love with Helena. Helena believes that Lysander is playing a cruel joke on her.

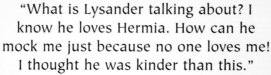

What might the characters be thinking ...?

"What is Lysander talking about? I know he loves Hermia. How can he mock me just because no one loves me! I thought he was kinder than this."

"Oh! I love her so much! I'd run through fire for her. Sweet Helena! How could I love that raven Hermia, when Helena is such a beautiful dove?"

Useful words ...

fond foolish (also: done for love)

repent regret

tedious boring

wherefore was I to this keen mockery born why do I deserve to be made fun of like this?

troth, sooth truth

woo try to win someone's love

perforce really

Enter Helena, running after Demetrius

HELENA … O, I am out of breath in this **fond** chase! …
But who is here? Lysander! on the ground!
Dead? or asleep? I see no blood, no wound.
Lysander, if you live, good sir, awake!

LYSANDER *(awaking)* And run through fire I will for thy sweet sake! …

HELENA Do not say so, Lysander; say not so …
Hermia still loves you: then be content.

LYSANDER Content with Hermia! No; I do **repent**
The **tedious** minutes I with her have spent.
Not Hermia, but Helena I love:
Who will not change a raven for a dove? …

HELENA **Wherefore was I to this keen mockery born?**
When at your hands did I deserve this scorn? …
Good **troth**, you do me wrong, good **sooth**, you do,
In such disdainful manner me to **woo**.
But fare you well; **perforce** I must confess
I thought you lord of more true gentleness …

Exit

LYSANDER She sees not Hermia. Hermia, sleep thou there:
And never mayst thou come Lysander near! …

Exit

17

The story ...

Bottom and the other actors are practising their play near where Titania is sleeping. Puck, on his way back to Oberon, hears them rehearsing and decides to have some fun. He waits until the script calls for Bottom to make an exit. Then Puck follows and, using his magic, gives Bottom a donkey's head. Bottom does not notice the difference, but when he re-enters his friends scream and run away, thinking he is some kind of monster. Bottom thinks his friends are playing a joke on him, and left alone in the forest, he sings to keep his courage up. His donkey noises wake Titania, who, because of the charm placed upon her, at once falls madly in love with Bottom.

What might the characters be thinking ...?

"I love you so much. Your singing is so beautiful, and you are so wise and attractive. My fairies will buy you every kind of treat and luxury. You must never leave me!"

"This is a bit odd! Why is she saying this? She might be a bit mad, but she seems very nice all the same!"

Useful words ...

enamour'd in love with

thy fair virtues force the fact that you are so good looking

wit intelligence

hop in his walks be ready to attend him wherever he goes

gambol in his eyes play in his view, to entertain him

dewberries gooseberries

do him courtesies be polite and helpful

18

The wood. Titania lying asleep

Enter Bottom with an ass's head

TITANIA *(awaking)*   What angel wakes me from my flowery bed?

BOTTOM *(sings)*

TITANIA   I pray thee, gentle mortal, sing again:
Mine ear is much **enamour'd** of thy note;
So is mine eye enthralled to thy shape;
And **thy fair virtue's force** perforce doth move me
On the first view to say, to swear, I love thee.

BOTTOM   Methinks, mistress, you should have little reason
for that: and yet, to say the truth, reason and
love keep little company together now-a-days …

TITANIA   Thou art as wise as thou art beautiful.

BOTTOM   Not so neither: but if I had **wit** enough to get out
of this wood, I have enough to serve mine own turn.

TITANIA   Out of this wood do not desire to go:
Thou shalt remain here, whether thou wilt or no.
And I do love thee. Therefore, go with me.
I'll give thee fairies to attend on thee,
And they shall fetch thee jewels from the deep,
And sing, while thou on pressed flowers dost sleep …
Peaseblossom! Cobweb! Moth! and Mustardseed! …

Enter Peaseblossom, Cobweb, Moth and Mustardseed

Be kind and courteous to this gentleman;
Hop in his walks and **gambol in his eyes**;
Feed him with apricots and **dewberries**,
With purple grapes, green figs, and mulberries;
The honey-bags steal from the humble-bees …
And pluck the wings from painted butterflies
To fan the moonbeams from his sleeping eyes.
Nod to him, elves, and **do him courtesies**.

The story ...

Puck returns to report to
Oberon that Titania has fallen in love
with a donkey, and that he has
charmed the young man from
Athens as instructed. But as they
talk two humans enter the clearing.
It is Hermia and Demetrius. Hermia
has awoken and has found Lysander
gone. In her search for Lysander she
has come across Demetrius.

What might the characters be thinking ...?

"A donkey! Wonderful! That'll show
Titania! This has worked out better
than I could have hoped. And now
here is the Athenian man I told
Puck to charm."

"I'm confused. This is the woman
I saw sleeping on the ground, but
not the man I cast a spell upon."

Useful words ...

dote on in extremity
be madly in love with

latch'd cast a spell on

20

Another part of the wood

Enter Oberon

OBERON I wonder if Titania be awaked;
Then, what it was that next came in her eye,
Which she must **dote on in extremity**.

Enter Puck

Here comes my messenger. How now, mad spirit? …

PUCK My mistress with a monster is in love …
Titania waked and straightway loved an ass.

OBERON This falls out better than I could devise.
But hast thou yet **latch'd** the Athenian's eyes
With the love-juice, as I did bid thee do?

PUCK I took him sleeping, – that is finish'd too, –
And the Athenian woman by his side …

Enter Hermia and Demetrius

OBERON Stand close: this is the same Athenian.

PUCK This is the woman, but not this the man.

21

The story ...

Hermia accuses Demetrius of killing Lysander and is very angry with him. Oberon realises that a mistake has been made and sends Puck to look for Helena, so that he can put things right.

What might the characters be thinking ...?

"Oh, my love! Lysander! Where are you? How I hate Demetrius!"

"Why is she so furious with me? I haven't touched Lysander. I don't even know where he is."

"This is Puck's fault; he has charmed the wrong man. We'd better sort this out."

"Something wrong here! I hope Oberon isn't angry with me."

Useful words ...

o'er shoes in blood over the tops of your shoes in blood

plunge in the deep get even deeper in blood

misprised mistaken

illusion magic

tartar in Shakespeare's time, a person from central Asia

22

HERMIA
… If thou hast slain Lysander in his sleep,
Being o'er shoes in blood, plunge in the deep,
And kill me too …

DEMETRIUS
You spend your passion on a **misprised** mood:
I am not guilty of Lysander's blood;
Nor is he dead, for aught that I can tell.

HERMIA
I pray thee, tell me then that he is well.

DEMETRIUS
And if I could, what should I get therefore?

HERMIA
A privilege never to see me more.
And from thy hated presence part I so:
See me no more, whether he be dead or no.

Exit

DEMETRIUS
There is no following her in this fierce vein:
Here therefore for a while I will remain …

OBERON
What hast thou done? Thou hast mistaken quite
And laid the love-juice on some true-love's sight …
About the wood go swifter than the wind,
And Helena of Athens look thou find …
By some **illusion** see thou bring her here:
I'll charm his eyes against she do appear.

PUCK
I go, I go; look how I go,
Swifter than arrow from the Tartar's bow. …

Exit

23

The story ...

As Puck flies off, Oberon places a spell of sleep upon Demetrius and drops the juices of the magic flower on to his eye-lids. Puck returns very soon, with Helena, and also with Lysander, who pursues Helena with cries of love. His shouting wakes up Demetrius who sees Helena and immediately falls in love with her again. Helena thinks that both men are mocking her and have planned the joke together. But both say that they are sincere. Demetrius and Lysander argue over Helena and prepare to fight. Puck reminds Oberon he must act quickly. Oberon instructs Puck to make the night with fog and lead the men away from each other. Puck must urge them to strike out at empty air until they get so weary that they lie down to sleep. Then the magic flower can be used on Lysander so that when he awakes and sees Hermia his love for her will return and the night will seem to all of them just a dream.

When this is done Oberon plans to go to Titania to ask her once again for the boy he wants.

What might the characters be thinking ...?

"I shall put things right so that the lovers will go back to Athens happily, thinking all their troubles were but a dream."

"We'd better get this sorted out quickly!"

Useful words ...

derision mockery

wend go

with league with agreement

night's swift dragons cut the clouds full fast night will soon be upon us

OBERON
... crush this herb into Lysander's eye;
Whose liquor hath this virtuous property,
To take from thence all error with his might,
And make his eyeballs roll with wonted sight.
When they next wake, all this **derision**
Shall seem a dream and fruitless vision,
And back to Athens shall the lovers **wend**,
With league whose date till death shall never end.
Whiles I in this affair do thee employ,
I'll to my Queen and beg her Indian boy;
And then I will her charmed eye release
From monster's view, and all things shall be peace.

Enter Puck

PUCK
My fairy lord, this must be done with haste,
For **night's swift dragons cut the clouds full fast** ...

OBERON
Puck, not withstanding, haste, make no delay;
We may effect this business yet ere day

Exit. Enter Lysander, Demetrius, Helena and Hermia in turn, following Puck
Each of them lies down and sleeps

PUCK
On the ground
Sleep sound:
I'll apply
To your eye,
Gentle lover, remedy. *(Squeezing the juice on Lysander's eyes)*

When thou wakest,
Thou takest
True delight
In the sight
Of thy former lady's eye:

The story ...

Oberon makes his way to Titania and Bottom. Titania, deeply in love, is stroking Bottom's very long ears. Bottom is ordering the fairies about as if they belonged to him.

What might the characters be thinking ...?

 "This is the life!"

 "Isn't he lovely!"

 "Is she mad? Is there anything else he can ask us to do?"

"This is going beyond a joke!"

Useful words ...

amiable friendly

coy caress, stroke

mounsieur mister

cavalery cavalier (a title of honour, rather like a knight)

PUCK	And the country proverb known,
	That every man should take his own,
	In your waking shall be shown:
	Jack shall have Jill;
	Nought shall go ill …

Exit

Enter Titania and Bottom; Peaseblossom, Cobweb, Moth, Mustardseed, and other Fairies attending; Oberon behind unseen

TITANIA	Come, sit thee down upon this flowery bed,
	While I thy **amiable** cheeks do **coy**,
	And stick musk-roses in thy sleek smooth head,
	And kiss thy fair large ears, my gentle joy.
BOTTOM	Where's Peaseblossom?
PEASEBLOSSOM	Ready.
BOTTOM	Scratch my head, Peaseblossom. Where's **Mounsieur** Cobweb?
COBWEB	Ready.
BOTTOM	Mounsieur Cobweb, good Mounsieur, get you your weapons in your hand, and kill me a red-hipped humble-bee on the top of a thistle; and, good Mounsieur, bring me the honey-bag … Where's Mounsieur Mustardseed?
MUSTARDSEED	Ready. … What's your will?
BOTTOM	Nothing, good Mounsieur, but to help **Cavalery** Cobweb to scratch. I must to the barber's, Monsieur; for methinks I am marvellous hairy about the face; and I am such a tender ass, if my hair do but tickle me, I must scratch …

The story ...

Oberon reveals himself to Titania and tells her off for her strange love. When Oberon asks for the serving boy, Titania agrees. The King accepts the boy and then casts a spell of sleep on Titania so he can remove the spell from her eyes. Oberon also orders Puck to take the donkey's head from Bottom so that when he wakes, he too will think that he has been dreaming.

What might the characters be thinking ...?

"Good! Now I've got the boy I'll make peace with Titania and sort everything out."

"I must cuddle up to this lovely donkey-man. Mmm ... I feel sleepy."

Useful words ...

venturous bold, adventurous

exposition Bottom is using a long word to try to impress, but it doesn't make sense

dotage foolishness

upbraid to tell off

transformed scalp changed head

swain a young man

repair travel

fierce vexation disturbance

wast wont used

TITANIA
Or say, sweet love, what thou desirest to eat …
I have a **venturous** fairy that shall seek
The squirrel's hoard, and fetch thee new nuts.

BOTTOM
I had rather have a handful or two of dried peas.
But, I pray you, let none of your people stir me: I
have an **exposition** of sleep come upon me.

TITANIA
Sleep thou, and I will wind thee in my arms.
Fairies, be gone, and be all ways away …
O, how I love thee! How I dote on thee!

Exeunt Fairies. Bottom and Titania sleep. Enter Puck

OBERON
Welcome, good Robin. See'st thou this sweet sight?
Her **dotage** now I do begin to pity;
For, meeting her of late behind the wood,
Seeking sweet favours for this hateful fool,
I did **upbraid** her and fall out with her …
When I had at my pleasure taunted her
And she in mild terms begg'd my patience,
I then did ask of her her changeling child;
Which straight she gave me, and her fairy sent
To bear him to my bower in fairy land.
And now I have the boy, I will undo
This hateful imperfection of her eyes.
And, gentle Puck, take this **transformed scalp**
From off the head of this Athenian **swain**,
That, he awaking when the other do,
May all to Athens back again **repair**,
And think no more of this night's accidents
But as the **fierce vexation** of a dream.
But first I will release the Fairy Queen. *(Touching her eyes)*

Be as thou **wast wont** to be;
See as thou wast wont to see …
Now, my Titania; wake you, my sweet Queen.

The story ...

The two happy couples (Lysander and Hermia; Helena and Demetrius) head back to Athens trying to untangle the events of last night, but they cannot decide what has been real and what has been a dream. Titania wakes and she and Oberon are friends again. Bottom is the last to wake and wonders at the strangeness of his dream. He heads back to the city to join his friends in the presentation of their play. Puck asks the audience for their applause and suggests that if they have not enjoyed the play then they can simply pretend that they have been asleep and dreaming.

What might the characters be thinking ...?

"Whatever has been going on? It's good to be friends with Oberon again."

"I've had a dream so strange it is beyond understanding."

"Not bad! I've got Titania again, and my new servant boy."

"Another good night's work!"

Useful words ...

enamour'd in love with

mortals humans

cue turn to speak in a play

ballad a story in song

give me your hands give me applause, clap your hands

restore amends make improvements to the play (in return for applause)

30

TITANIA	My Oberon! What visions have I seen! Methought I was **enamour'd** of an ass.
OBERON	There lies your love … Robin, take off this head …
PUCK	Now, when thou wakest, with thine own fool's eyes peep.
OBERON	Sound, music! Come, my queen, take hands with me, And rock the ground whereon these sleepers be …
PUCK	Fairy King, attend, and mark: I do hear the morning lark …
TITANIA	Come, my lord, and in our flight, Tell me how it came this night That I sleeping here was found, With these **mortals** on the ground.

Exeunt

BOTTOM *(awaking)* When my **cue** comes, call me, and I will
answer. … Peter Quince! Flute, the bellows-mender! Snout,
the tinker! Starveling! God's my life, stolen
hence, and left me asleep! I have had a most rare
vision. I have had a dream, past the wit of man to
say what dream it was. Man is but an ass, if he go
about to expound this dream. …
I will get Peter Quince to write a **ballad** of this dream: it shall
be called 'Bottom's Dream', because it hath no bottom …

Exit

Act V, Scene 1

PUCK

If we shadows have offended,
Think but this, and all is mended,
That you have but slumber'd here
While these visions did appear …
So, good night unto you all.
Give me your hands, if we be friends,
And Robin shall **restore amends**.

Exit

31

The end of the story

That night there are three weddings: the wedding of Duke
Theseus and also the wedding of Hermia to Lysander, and Helena
to Demetrius. The couples tell their strange story to the Duke
who shakes his head, unbelieving.

Then, to end the evening, the Duke calls for entertainment.
Peter Quince and his friends, including Nick Bottom, put on their
play. Bottom of course receives the lion's share of the attention.